Once a Week Comprehension

Formerly 'Once a Week'

BOOK TWO

By HAYDN PERRY

Diploma in English Literature, University of London
formerly Headmaster, Merryhills School, Enfield

D1639012

GINN AND COMPANY LTD

© Haydn Perry 1960

Without Answers
Thirty-ninth impression 1996 029606
ISBN 0 602 20711 8

With Answers
ISBN 0 602 22421 7

Published by Ginn and Company
Prebendal House, Parson's Fee
Aylesbury, Bucks HP20 2QY

Printed in Great Britain by
Henry Ling Ltd, Dorchester, Dorset

PREFACE

This book of English tests is intended for third-year pupils of Primary Schools. It can be used either for testing progress and ability, or it can serve as a textbook from which pupils can work alone or with the teacher's help.

In each of the thirty tests, the first question is of the comprehension type. These questions test the reading and reasoning of the pupils. More than sixty other types of questions are included in these books. All branches of English suitable for the age-group are thus adequately tested.

TO THE PUPIL

In each of the thirty tests there are five questions.

Read each question carefully, so that you understand exactly what you are asked to do before you begin.

Do not spend too long on any one question. You should answer all five questions in 45 minutes.

Make sure that you have not missed a question, or part of one.

If you find that you have made a mistake, alter your work clearly and neatly so that your teacher will know what it is you mean him to read and mark.

HAYDN PERRY

TEST 1

I. Read very carefully through the following passage, and then answer the questions.

The Battle of Hastings

At the Battle of Hastings the English, who were led by Harold, had taken up the best position at the top of Senlac Hill. The Norman soldiers tried repeatedly to dislodge them, but the English had driven wooden stakes into the ground and, from the shelter of these, they were able to force their enemies back down the hill time and time again.

William the Norman, whom we now call William the Conqueror, decided he would try to win the battle by other means. He ordered his archers to shoot their arrows high into the air so that they would fall on to the heads of the English. In time, many defenders were killed in this way.

The greatest disaster came when an arrow pierced the eye of the English king himself. Harold fell to the ground and his soldiers, seeing their leader slain, fled from the hill in confusion. So died Harold, The Last of the English Kings.

1. Who were the two leaders in this battle?
2. What other names are given to these two leaders?
3. Where did the battle take place: (a) on the banks of a river; (b) on the slopes of a hill; (c) around the walls of a castle?
4. Why was it difficult for the Normans to drive out the English?
5. What plan did the Normans use in an effort to gain the victory?
6. Why had the shooting of arrows in the usual way proved to be a failure?
7. What was **the greatest disaster**?
8. What words or phrases in the story mean (a) drive them out; (b) stuck into; (c) in fear and disorder?

4

9. Why did the Normans not use their cannon: (a) because they had left them behind in Normandy; (b) because the English had captured them; (c) because gunpowder and cannon had not been invented at that time?
10. Why did the English finally run away?
11. Were the defenders (a) the Normans, led by William; (b) the people who were looking on; (c) the English, led by Harold?

II. When we wish to say that something is **red,** we may say **as red as blood.**

Choose the correct answers from these:

1. As black as (a) a mole; (b) a hole; (c) coal.
2. As brown as (a) a lorry; (b) a berry; (c) a beret.
3. As green as (a) grass; (b) paint; (c) a carpet.
4. As blue as (a) a butterfly; (b) the sky; (c) a gate.

III. Here are two words, **rock** and **garden.** From these we can make the word **rock-garden.**

Make four new compound words from the following:

spinning	tea	lace	alarm
shoe	fire	wheel	spoon

IV. A number of **chicks** together is called a **brood.** What words could be used for:

1. A number of herring
2. A number of bees
3. A number of buffaloes
4. A number of birds

V. Rewrite these sentences so that they mean **more than one.**

Example: The **tree** grew tall. The **trees** grew tall.

1. The day and night seemed long.
2. The berry lay near the leaf.
3. The bird sat on the chimney.
4. The monkey bit the lady.
5. The watch lay in the gutter.

TEST 2

I. Read very carefully through the following passage, and then answer the questions.

Theras

Theras was seven years old, and because he was seven he was to go to school. That was the custom of the city in which he lived. It was an exciting day for everyone in the house, most of all for Theras. Until this time he had had to stay at home with his mother and the servants, and was allowed to play only in the house, or in the street close by the front door. Now he was to go out to school with the other boys. Now he would often be with his father, going to and fro in the city. He already felt grown up.

Now to start. Theras's mother put on him his long, outdoor cloak; for in the house he wore only one garment, like a shirt, reaching to his knees. His mother kissed him. You might have thought he was going miles away.

C. D. Snedeker

1. What important thing was happening to Theras?
2. Why was this to happen?
3. With whom had he always been until this time?
4. Where had he been allowed to play?
5. What garment would he wear out of doors?
6. Why might you have thought he was going miles away: (*a*) because of his outdoor clothes; (*b*) because of the fuss his mother made of him; (*c*) because he really was going miles away?
7. Why did he feel **grown up**: (*a*) because he had suddenly grown tall; (*b*) because his father carried him on his shoulders; (*c*) because he was going to and fro in the city?
8. Write down the sentences that are **true**: (*a*) Theras lived in a small village. (*b*) He lived in a foreign country. (*c*) He lived in a city. (*d*) He lived in England. (*e*) His parents were wealthy. (*f*) He came from a poor family.

II. There are mistakes in each of these sentences. Write the sentences correctly:

1. He is taller than me.
2. Could you see who done it?
3. He sang that song very nice.
4. The teacher rung the bell at twelve o'clock.
5. The match had just began.

III. Rewrite these sentences using **single words** instead of the phrases that are in heavy type:

1. The concert was **put off until another day.**
2. They left by the door marked **Way Out.**
3. The sky was **without a cloud.**
4. Ann had **great numbers of** friends.
5. John **made up his mind** to win the prize.

IV. The opposite of **come** is **go.** Write out these sentences using the opposite of the word in heavy type to fill each space:

1. You must either **accept** or —— the honour.
2. The valley was **near;** the mountainside was ——.
3. This sum is **easy,** but that one is ——.
4. They were led from **danger** to ——.
5. Do you come here **often?** No, very ——.

V. Write out in full the **abbreviations** (shortened forms) shown in these sentences:

1. He was out **l.b.w.** playing for England at Lord's.
2. It is for the **N.S.P.C.C.** to decide, not the **R.S.P.C.A.**
3. **H.R.H.** the Prince of Wales may visit the headquarters of the **E.E.C.**
4. The envelope marked **O.H.M.S.** was sent to the **M.P.** at the Houses of Parliament.

TEST 3

I. Read very carefully through the following passage, and then answer the questions.

The Stream

The first rays of the rising sun awoke the sleeping flowers on the hillside. The pink rose-bay willow-herb, the scarlet poppy, and the convolvulus with its white bells all seemed to glance upwards and stir themselves for another day. The stream, too, seemed to rouse itself, and sparkle more brightly as it dashed towards the river in the valley below. The sedges in the shallows moved gently to and fro, and the water-weed took on new shapes in the sunlight.

The colony of moorhens in their reedy home knew that it was time to be out and about in search of food, fun and adventure. The chicks became more and more daring as time went on, and darted here, there and everywhere, whilst their mothers kept careful watch in case enemies, two-footed or four-footed, should try to harm them.

1. What was it that woke the sleeping flowers?
2. What flowers are named in the story?
3. Which of the plants has a bell-shaped flower?
4. To where was the stream dashing?
5. What happened to the water plants when the sun shone?
   (a) They died from the heat. (b) They took on new shapes.
   (c) They went back to sleep. Which?
6. Who lived in the reeds?
7. What three things might the moorhens look for?
8. How did the chicks behave as the day went on?
9. What were their mothers doing at this time?
10. What kinds of enemies were feared: (a) animals only; (b) humans only; (c) animals and human beings?

11. Write down, from this list, the words that describe the young hens: brave, high-spirited, cowardly, timid, daring, careful, fearless.

II. We call **one and only** a word-double. (He is the **one and only** champion.) Complete these sentences with the correct word-doubles:

1. They fought back **time and** ——.
2. The car went by **fits and** ——.
3. Brian stood **head and** —— above his friends.
4. Everything must be **spick and** —— before the bell goes.

III. Here are five sentences from a story, but they are not in the order in which things happened. Write them in the correct order.

1. It was very heavy.
2. As Jane walked along she saw a parcel in the gutter.
3. She took it to the police-station.
4. She stooped to pick it up.
5. It was placed in a special cupboard.

IV. HE is a **masculine** word. Its partner SHE is a **feminine** word. In the following sentences, write **feminine** words in place of the **masculine** words shown in heavy type.

1. The **emperor** helped the **prince.**
2. The **husband** saw the **gentleman** to the door.
3. The **actor** is a **bachelor.**
4. **Sir, he** is a **traitor.**

V. **Punctuation marks** (full stops, capital letters, etc.) have been omitted from the following sentences. Rewrite the sentences correctly:

1. good morning said the boy
2. have you a belt the man asked
3. did you see lions tigers elephants and apes at the zoo
4. its a boundary cried the boy

9

TEST 4

I. Read very carefully through the following passage, and then answer the questions.

On the Desert Island

Two sailors named Pat and Mike fell overboard from a ship, but managed to swim to an island. They roamed about in search of human beings, but found that the island was uninhabited. There wasn't even a hut where they could shelter for the night, so they lay down in the shade of a palm-tree, and were soon fast asleep.

After some time, however, they were awakened by swarms of mosquitoes which came from a nearby lake. These ferocious insects bit them so much that sleep was out of the question. "Let's pull our coats over our heads, and perhaps they'll go away," Pat suggested.

They did so, and for some time all went well until Mike, being curious, looked out and saw some fireflies hovering overhead. "It's no use hiding any longer, Pat," he cried, "they're looking for us with lanterns!"

1. How was it that the men were on the island?
2. What did they first try to find?
3. What did they do when they found their search was useless?
4. Write down the sentences that are **true**: (a) They slept until dawn next day. (b) They heard the roaring of lions. (c) They were awakened immediately. (d) They awoke some hours later. (e) Their sleep was disturbed by cannibals. (f) Fierce, stinging insects awoke them.
5. What did Pat suggest was a way of getting to sleep?
6. Why did Mike look out: (a) because he wanted something to eat; (b) because he had forgotten to wind the alarm-clock; (c) because he was curious as to what was going on?
7. What did Mike see when he looked out?
8. What did he believe was happening?

II. Odd man out. In each of the following groups of words, one is out of place because it has nothing to do with the others. Write down that word.

Example: oak, ash, **banana**, elm. **Banana** is odd man out because it is a fruit, and the other three are trees.

Find the **odd man out** in these:

1. Jennifer, Mary, Francis, Jane
2. pansy, marigold, violet, tulip
3. hut, caravan, bungalow, house
4. bus, sedan-chair, car, taxi

III. This is to **that.**

Example: **Sailor** is to **navy** as **soldier** is to ——. **(army)**
Now complete these:

1. **Fingers** are to **man** as —— are to **lion.**
2. **Cup** is to **saucer** as **knife** is to ——.
3. **Walk** is to **legs** as **fly** is to ——.
4. **Radio** is to **ear** as **television** is to ——.

IV. Here are some **crossword-puzzle clues,** and a part of each answer. Complete the words:

1. A plank of wood.   B---D
2. Not dear in price.   CH--P
3. Rough and unpolished.   C--RSE
4. To pretend to make an attack, as in a boxing   F-INT
   match.

V. Write down the answers to the following questions:

1. What would you expect to find in a scabbard?
2. What is a place called where grapes are grown?
3. What is the work of a milliner?
4. On what would one play the game of bowls?
5. To what kind of shop should I go to buy bread?

11

TEST 5

I. Read very carefully through the following verses, and then answer the questions.

Sir Ralph the Rover

Sir Ralph the Rover sailed away,
He scoured the sea for many a day;
And now grown rich with plundered store,
He steers his course for Scotland's shore.

So thick a haze o'erspreads the sky,
They cannot see the sun on high;
The wind has blown a gale all day,
At evening it hath died away.

On the deck the Rover takes his stand,
So dark it is they see no land.
Quoth Sir Ralph, "It will be lighter soon,
For there is the dawn of the rising moon."

Robert Southey

1. Sir Ralph was (*a*) a peaceful trader; (*b*) a merchantman; (*c*) a pirate; (*d*) an explorer. Which of these?
2. How do we know that he had made a long voyage?
3. How can we tell that the weather was foggy?
4. What had the weather been like during the day?
5. Sir Ralph was (*a*) up the mainmast; (*b*) in the crow's nest; (*c*) below; (*d*) standing on deck; (*e*) climbing the rigging. Which is correct?
6. What was he hoping to see?
7. He was making his way (*a*) towards Britain; (*b*) to the South Seas; (*c*) up a river. Which is true?
8. Why was it going to be lighter soon: (*a*) because they were going to light a lantern; (*b*) because the sun was coming up; (*c*) because the moon was rising?
9. What words or phrases in the story mean (*a*) wanderer; (*b*) passed swiftly over; (*c*) mist; (*d*) covers; (*e*) said?

12

II. When we say that we have 'nipped something in the bud' we mean that we have put an end to something before it became serious. 'Nipped in the bud' is an **everyday expression.**

In the following, choose the phrase that means nearly the same as the everyday expression:

1. **To weigh anchor** means: (*a*) the way into a harbour; (*b*) to find the weight of a ship's anchor; (*c*) to haul up the anchor before setting sail.
2. **To bury the hatchet** means: (*a*) to make peace; (*b*) to hide the axe in the woodshed; (*c*) to have a funeral.
3. **A leap in the dark** means: (*a*) to go into a dark room; (*b*) to do something without having thought very carefully about it; (*c*) to take part in a high-jump competition at night.

III. **Sound-words** are missing from this sentence. Choose suitable words to fill the spaces:

As the —— of the drum stopped, the door ——, and the — of a cane was heard above the —— of the clock.

IV. Here are some famous football teams. Write them in **alphabetical order.**

Southampton, Tranmere, Arsenal, Tottenham, Blackpool, Cardiff, Bolton, Manchester United, Manchester City, Southend.

V. **Choosing suitable words**

1. Here are four **nouns:** hill, cat, result, voice.

And here are four **adjectives,** words that describe them: gruff, sleek, correct, steep.

Write the words together in suitable pairs.

2. Here are four other **adjectives:** handsome, painful, plentiful, foaming.

Here are four **nouns:** torrent, prince, supply, illness.

Write them together in suitable pairs.

TEST 6

Read very carefully through the following passage, and then answer the questions.

King Alfred

Of the many historical tales we are told the best known, without doubt, is that of Alfred and the cakes. Alfred, defeated by the Danes, and separated from his army, had taken refuge in the hut of a cowherd. The peasant and his wife did not know that the poor, hungry traveller was their king, and the woman had told him to keep an eye on some cakes that were baking at the side of the open fire.

It seems that Alfred, deep in thought as to how he could defeat his enemies, forgot about the cakes, and when the peasant-woman came back from the cow-byre, there they were, each burnt to a cinder. He was soundly scolded by the angry woman. But all ended well when some of Alfred's nobles came upon the scene and told her that the careless visitor was the king.

1. Why had Alfred taken refuge in the hut?
2. Which of these might the cowherd and his wife have said? (*a*) "What do you want, stranger?" (*b*) "Welcome, Your Majesty, to our hut." (*c*) "Would you like to rest for a while until your generals come along?"
3. What special job was Alfred given to do?
4. Why did Alfred fail to do his job properly?
5. How did the woman show her anger?
6. How did she find out who her visitor was?
7. Write down the sentences that are **true**: (*a*) The cakes were laid on the hearth near the fire. (*b*) They were in separate tins in the oven. (*c*) They were burned because the gas was turned up too high. (*d*) They were burned because Alfred forgot to watch them. (*e*) The cakes were being cooked over the fire.

14

8. What words or phrases in the story mean (*a*) had gone to safety; (*b*) a man who looks after cows; (*c*) the barn?

II. Some words have a similar sound, but are spelt differently. Example: 'The cats' **paws**', and 'There was a moment's **pause**'.

In the sentences below, choose the correct word from those inside the brackets:

1. Joan of Arc was burned at the (**stake, steak**).
2. The bride and bridegroom walked down the (**isle, aisle**).
3. The wine was stored in a dark (**seller, cellar**).
4. He made the parcel secure with (**ceiling, sealing**) wax.

III. **In** and **pin** are rhyming words, because they have the same sound. Write these twelve words in pairs, so that they rhyme.

beer   gnash   gaol   psalm   caught   calm
pail   brought   crash   draught   pier   raft

IV. Look at this word—**small**. Now look at the three words inside this bracket—(great, little, wise). The word nearest in meaning to small is **little**, so we choose that.

Do the same with these, choosing **one word** from inside the bracket each time:

1. **buy**   (lose, purchase, lend)
2. **proud**   (haughty, mean, careless)
3. **reveal**   (hide, show, buy)
4. **pedestrian**   (cyclist, airman, walker)

V. Look at the word BIRD. A bird need not be **large**. It need not have **webbed feet**, but it must have **wings**.

Choose one word from those in the brackets that **always** has to do with the word before the bracket:

1. **racket**   (press, strings, guarantee)
2. **watch**   (chain, face, strap)
3. **school**   (tower, playing-fields, pupils)
4. **knife**   (blade, silver, sheath)

TEST 7

I. Read very carefully through the following passage, and then answer the questions.

The Ant and the Dove

Once, an ant who had come to drink at a stream fell into the water and was carried away by the swift current. He was in great danger of drowning. A dove, perched on a nearby tree, saw the ant's peril and dropped a leaf into the water. The ant clambered on to this, and was carried to safety.

Some time after this a hunter, creeping through the bushes, spied the dove asleep, and took careful aim with his musket. He was about to fire when the ant, who was near by, crawled forward and bit him sharply in the ankle. The hunter missed his aim, and the loud report of the gun awakened the dove from her sleep. She saw her danger and flew swiftly away to safety. Thus the ant repaid the dove for having saved his life in the foaming current of the stream.

1. What brought the ant to the stream?
2. Where was the dove at that moment?
3. What was it that made a lifeboat for the ant?
4. Why was the dove in danger?
5. How did the ant startle the hunter?
6. What was the huntsman armed with: (a) a bow and arrow; (b) a spear; (c) a kind of rifle; (d) a net?
7. The ant was in danger because: (a) the current was flowing swiftly; (b) it had struck its head; (c) the dove was seeking to kill it; (d) the bridge had broken down.
8. From this list choose words and phrases that describe the ant in the water: tiny, struggling, swimming contentedly, at his last gasp, at ease, given up for lost.

II. The words in each of the following are in wrong order. Rearrange them to make sentences. (There may be more than one answer in some cases):

1. Stable the horse into put the.
2. Knife and your lend me fork.
3. Nail the strike hammer the with.
4. From the scent a sweet came bottle.

III. Each of the answers to the following clues begins with the letters SAL. Write down the words.

1. A person's wages.   SAL - - -
2. A fish.   SAL - - -
3. Can be made from fruit, or vegetables.   SAL - -
4. Used to season your food.   SAL -
5. Goods recovered after damage.   SAL - - - -

IV. The word **ball** has more than one meaning. It may mean 'a grand dance'; or it may mean 'a round object often used in games'.

Write down the words that fit in with the following descriptions:

1. A web-footed bird; to lower one's head quickly; a score of no runs at cricket.
2. To hit something; to stop work, and refuse to go back.
3. A piece of wood in the ground; the delivery of letters.
4. Something tied in a rope or string; a mark in wood.
5. The bottom of a shoe; a flat-fish; the only one.

V. Choose, from the words in brackets, the most suitable word to finish the line of poetry:

We are three Lords come out of Spain
That we may court your daughter (**Ann, Jill, Jane**).
My daughter Jane is far too young,
And cannot bear your flattering (**voice, tongue, tone, speech**).
The fairest one that we can see
Is pretty Nancy. Come to (**Spain, dinner, me, us**).

TEST 8

I. Read very carefully through the following passage, and then answer the questions.

Theras Looks On

Theras stopped before a shop which was open all along the front of it. What fun it was to see the man squatting at the wheel, and making a pot out of soft clay. The wheel, made of solid wood, no spokes, lay flat before him like a table, and all the while the potter kept whirling it, whirling it. Then he slapped down a handful of clay on the middle of the wheel, and smoothed the whirling mass into a round shape. With both hands the potter pressed its sides, and it grew tall; then he put his fist in the middle, and it grew hollow. All the time it quivered and trembled. The clay certainly seemed alive. Already it had a base, and a pretty slender neck. Then the man squeezed it boldly, and with one more touch it changed into a pitcher. Surely that was magic.

C. D. Snedeker

1. How was the shop different from other shops? It had (*a*) double windows; (*b*) no windows; (*c*) stained-glass windows; (*d*) circular windows. Which of these?
2. What was the man inside the shop making?
3. How do we know that he was not sitting down to his work?
4. What material was he using: (*a*) plasticine; (*b*) plywood; (*c*) raffia; (*d*) balsa wood; (*e*) clay?
5. When the worker pressed the sides, what happened? (*a*) The object grew taller. (*b*) It collapsed. (*c*) It changed colour. (*d*) It disappeared. Which?
6. What made the clay seem to be alive? (*a*) It made a noise. (*b*) It changed its shape so quickly. (*c*) It had limbs like a human being.
7. This all seemed magic to Theras because: (*a*) the worker kept on saying magic words; (*b*) the clay kept on taking fresh shapes; (*c*) the man really was a magician. Why?

8. Write down the sentences that are **true:** (*a*) The wheel had a number of spokes. (*b*) Theras was happy at what he saw. (*c*) The workman had someone to help him. (*d*) The wheel was quite solid. (*e*) The man was a marvellous craftsman.

II. The three words in the first bracket have similar meanings. Choose **one word** from those in the second bracket that is also similar in meaning to those in the first bracket.

Example: (**look, see, observe**)—(taste, **behold**, follow)

1. (request, ask, beg)—(crave, give, know)
2. (weak, feeble, delicate)—(powerful, frail, strong)
3. (folk, people, persons)—(humans, things, objects)
4. (doctor, surgeon, specialist)—(miner, grocer, physician)

III. We speak of **a** girl and **a** street, but **an** egg and **an** orange.

Write **a** or **an** in the spaces in the following sentences.

1. —— Englishman and —— Greek travelled in —— old train.
2. Lend me —— oilskin instead of —— coat.
3. Here's —— ticket for —— exhibition.
4. —— rasher and —— egg make —— appetizing meal.

IV. Complete these **proverbs** or well-known sayings:

1. Two heads are better —— ——.
2. A stitch in time —— ——.
3. All's well —— —— ——.
4. Better late —— ——.

V. Rewrite this paragraph beginning each **proper noun** with a **capital letter.**

Long ago robin hood and his men lived in sherwood forest, near nottingham. In those days you would have seen friar tuck and little john in the greenwood. Once, king richard the lion-heart visited the robbers' camp, a long way from london.

TEST 9

I. Read very carefully through the following passage, and then answer the questions.

The Thames

The River Thames rises in the Cotswolds and flows in a south-easterly direction. On its way to the sea it passes through many well-known places, including Oxford, Windsor and Richmond. Every year one of the most famous races in the world takes place on its waters—the Oxford and Cambridge boat race. The race starts at Putney and ends at Mortlake. The length of the course is 7·24 kilometres.

The Thames flows through the counties of Gloucestershire, Oxfordshire, Berkshire, Buckinghamshire, Middlesex, Surrey, Kent and Essex. It flows through lovely countryside and past world-famous buildings such as Hampton Court, Windsor Castle, the Houses of Parliament and the Tower of London. In olden times the Thames was the main highway through London. Queen Elizabeth I was often rowed upon it in her State Barge. Then there were no stone embankments, and London Bridge was the only bridge.

1. In what hills does the Thames rise?
2. In what direction does it flow?
3. Name three well-known places through which it passes.
4. (*a*) Where does the Boat Race begin? (*b*) Where does it end? (*c*) How long is the course? (*d*) Who takes part in this race?
5. Name the counties through which the Thames flows.
6. **It was the main highway through London.** Does this mean: (*a*) The Thames was higher than it is today. (*b*) It flowed through pipes, like a water-main. (*c*) It was the easiest way to travel through London?
7. Under which of these bridges did Queen Elizabeth pass: Tower Bridge, Westminster Bridge, London Bridge, Waterloo Bridge?

8. Write down the sentences that are **true**: (*a*) The State Barge could not move when the wind was not blowing. (*b*) Everyone could use the State Barge. (*c*) The State Barge belonged to the Queen. (*d*) The State Barge was propelled by oars. (*e*) The Royal Coach of today does the same job as the State Barge did then. (*f*) Queen Elizabeth rowed the State Barge.

II. From the words **inside the bracket** in each sentence, write down the one word that is nearest in meaning to the word in front of the sentence.

Example: **refuge.** They took (dinner, **shelter,** root) in the hut.

1. **innocent**   John is (guilty, blameless, careless).
2. **contented**   He was always a (disturbed, happy, restless) baby.
3. **protect**   The dog will (annoy, chase, guard) the flock.
4. **prompt**   Please send me a (careful, speedy, lengthy) reply.

III. Peas, beans, carrots and turnips are all **vegetables.** Write down a general name for each of these groups:
1. pepper, mustard, salt, vinegar
2. tea, coffee, sugar, flour
3. football, tennis, cricket, hockey
4. bracelet, earrings, necklace, brooch
5. tiger, lion, panther, puma

IV. Write these **in order of size,** beginning with the smallest.
1. sentence, letter, paragraph, chapter
2. dessert spoon, coffee spoon, teaspoon, tablespoon
3. turnip, marrow, pea, onion
4. pigeon, thrush, swan, wren

V. In each case, rearrange the letters of the words so as to make the name of a fruit. Example: CHEAP becomes PEACH.
1. P P L E A   2. N N A B A A
3. R R E Y C H   4. P A G R E

TEST 10

I. Read very carefully through the following verses, and then answer the questions.

The Pigtail

There lived a sage in days of yore,
And he a handsome pigtail wore,
But wondered much, and sorrowed more,
Because it hung behind him.

He mused upon this curious case,
And swore he'd change the pigtail's place,
And have it hanging at his face,
Not dangling there behind him.

Said he, "The mystery I've found;
I'll turn me round."—He turned him round:
But still it hung behind him.

H. W. Thackeray

1. Write down the **four words** which tell us that this was happening some time ago.
2. What was worrying the man in the story: (*a*) that his eyesight was failing him; (*b*) that his hair was getting thin; (*c*) that his cheeks had grown pale; (*d*) that his pigtail was hanging at the back of him?
3. What was he trying so hard to do?
4. How did he think that he would be able to do this?
5. Write the line which tells us that he did not succeed in doing so.
6. A sage is (*a*) a man who grows herbs in a garden; (*b*) a man who drives a coach; (*c*) a wise and learned man; (*d*) a man who lives amongst the sage-bushes in the garden. Which of these?
7. Write down the words and phrases that describe the way in which the man was behaving: foolishly wisely, in an extraordinary way, in an unusual way, in a peculiar way, happily.
8. Write in full: I've, I'll.

II. Read through this passage very carefully, and then write it down as it should be written, in verse. Begin each new line with a **capital letter.**

Gaily bedight, a gallant knight, in sunshine and in shadow, had journeyed long, singing a song, in search of El Dorado.

III. Beginning with the word BAD, and changing only one letter at a time, we can make the word COT.

Example: BAD, CAD, CAT, COT.

In the same way, change the word HARD into the word EASY.

HARD

1. One of a pack of 52. CARD
2. We drive a horse and ----
3. To throw (a stone?) ----
4. Opposite of west. ----

EASY

IV. **Country**—France **People**—French **Language**—French
Now complete these lists:

Country	**People**	**Language**
1. England		
2. China		
3. Sweden		
4. Italy		

V. Name these people of whom we read in a book or poem.

1. He was made thrice mayor of London.
2. He was Robinson Crusoe's companion.
3. He was brought up by wolves.
4. He was a very mean man, especially at Christmas-time.
5. She fell down a rabbit-hole.
6. He lived in Sherwood Forest.

TEST 11

I. Read very carefully through the following passage, and then answer the questions.

The Village Shop

Our village shop sold an astonishing number of things. You could buy almost anything you wanted there from bootlaces to bull's-eyes, from tea-cosies to corn-cure. If the articles wanted didn't happen to be in stock, without hesitation Miss Murchison would say "I can get it for you". We often wondered if she would say this if we asked for an elephant, or Captain Silver's parrot. We were too scared to put this to the test.

On one occasion Jim Judd, because of the slow way in which the shop was run, fastened a tortoise to the front door as a hint to the proprietor. But Miss Murchison took not the slightest notice of this, and carried on as usual, moving in her careful manner from one customer to another, enquiring about each one's illness, or how the children were getting on at school.

1. Write down the sentences that are **true:** (a) The shop sold articles of one kind only. (b) The shop was situated in a large town. (c) Miss Murchison rushed madly from one part of the shop to another. (d) It was almost certain that the shop had what you wanted. (e) Within the shop it was peaceful.
2. Write down the names of the four things mentioned as being in stock.
3. What were the two unusual things for which we thought of asking?
4. What did Miss Murchison say if an article was out of stock?
5. How did Jim Judd show that he was not satisfied?
6. What effect did this have on Miss Murchison?
7. In what two things was Miss Murchison interested when she spoke to customers?

8. Divide the words below into two lists: (a) those that describe Jim Judd, and (b) those that describe Miss Murchison: calm, playful, impatient, restless, quiet, kindly, comical, tender-hearted, placid, humorous.

II. A **splinter** is **a very small piece of wood.** Here are some other small amounts:

scrap   drop   pinch   speck

Choose the correct ones to use with these words:

salt   dirt   rain   paper

III. Below are pairs of sentences. Join each pair by using one of the following words: **which, who, when, where.** You may have to rearrange the words in some cases.

1. John will go to Brighton. He will meet his friend.
2. Everyone has heard of Wellington. He was the hero of Waterloo.
3. He had begun shouting. The police came in.
4. St. Paul's Cathedral is in London. It was built by Wren.

IV. Complete the words below by adding **ery** or **ary**, whichever is correct:

1. John went to read the books in the **libr ---**.
2. The ball was lost in the **shrubb ---**.
3. The funeral went on its way to the **cemet ---**.
4. On the edge of the moor stood a **solit ---** cottage.

V. Below is a story. The words in heavy type show that it is taking place **now.** Change these words so that the story happened **in the past.**

The coach **draws** up at the inn, and the only passenger **dismounts.** He **gives** his coat a shake, and then **passes** into the dining-room, where a fire **burns** in the grate, and hot coffee **awaits** him. The coach **goes** on its way, and the innkeeper **stares** after it.

TEST 12

I. **Read** very carefully through the following passage, and then answer the questions.

The Frogs

Some frogs who lived in a large pond wished very much to have a king to rule over them, but they could not decide which of them should be chosen. So they asked Jupiter, the king of the gods, to send them a king. Jupiter, saying "This is your king", dropped a heavy log, with a great splash, into the pool. After a time the frogs grew used to the log which only floated there and did nothing else. So they asked Jupiter for a new king, one who would be more exciting.

This time Jupiter sent them a stork to rule over them, and it was not long before the new king was moving about amongst his subjects, gobbling up as many as he could catch. The frogs fled in terror to the bottom of the pool. They asked Jupiter to take away their cruel king. But Jupiter refused to do so.

1. (*a*) Where did the frogs live? (*b*) What did they wish for?
2. Why didn't they choose a frog for a king?
3. Who was Jupiter?
4. How did King Log show that he had arrived?
5. Why were the frogs not satisfied with the log as a king?
6. The second king was (*a*) a lifeless object; (*b*) a human being; (*c*) a live creature. Which of these?
7. How did the stork show that he was the master of the frogs?
8. Where did the frogs take refuge?
9. What did the frogs then ask Jupiter to do?
10. Write down the statements that are **true**: (*a*) The frogs were peaceful and contented. (*b*) They were always wanting something different. (*c*) They lived in a swift-flowing river. (*d*) Jupiter helped them each time they asked him to. (*e*) The stork was a merciless ruler.

II. Look at this sentence: Where is Jims ball? The **apostrophe** is missing. The sentence should be: Where is Jim's ball?

Put the **apostrophe** in its correct place in each of the following sentences:

1. This is Bettys doll.
2. Have you read 'King Solomons Mines'?
3. You have spoilt the childs game.
4. You have spoilt the childrens game.
5. Are you the boys (more than one) mother?

III. Look at these two sentences:

(*a*) Alice asked: "Where is it?"
(*b*) Alice asked where it was.

In the first sentence Alice **speaks the words.** In the second sentence she does not actually speak. Change the following sentences so that the people are **actually speaking.**

1. The boy said that he was afraid.
2. The crowd shouted that it was a goal.
3. The girl said that she was eleven.
4. The explorer said that he was lost.

IV. When we hear the word **collar** we often think of the word **tie.** Write down the words which go with the following:

1. Shoes and ——   4. Blouse and ——
2. Pants and ——   5. Arms and ——
3. Doublet and ——   6. Pen and ——

V. Each of the following words begins with **ph** that sounds as **f.**

1. King in ancient Egypt
2. A ghost, or shadowy creature
3. A group of words, not a sentence
4. A person who takes pictures

TEST 13

I. Read very carefully through the following passages, and then answer the questions.

The Journey

We wended our way back to the coast, intending to encamp near the beach, for the mosquitoes were troublesome in the forest. We could not help admiring the birds which flew and chirped around us. Among them we observed a pretty kind of parakeet with a green body and a blue head, a few beautiful turtle-doves, and several flocks of wood-pigeons. The hues of many of these birds were very vivid—bright green, blue and scarlet. We made several attempts to bring down one of the birds, both with the bow and sling, to find whether they were good for food. But we always missed, although once or twice we were very near hitting.

As evening drew on, however, a flock of pigeons flew past. I slung a stone into the midst of them, and had the good fortune to hit one.

R. M. Ballantyne

1. Why did they wish to encamp near the beach, and not in the forest?
2. Write down the sentences that are **true**: (*a*) They hurried back. (*b*) They strolled back. (*c*) They hastened back. (*d*) They ran back. (*e*) They wandered back. (*f*) They rode back. (*g*) They ambled back.
3. What birds did they see whilst returning?
4. Which of these are correct? (*a*) The birds were plain in colour. (*b*) The birds were brightly coloured. (*c*) The birds' feathers were dazzling. (*d*) There was nothing very striking about the birds. (*e*) They took no notice of the birds. (*f*) They looked with interest at the birds.
5. What did they make several attempts to do?
6. How do we know that they were not successful?

7. They did not succeed because: (*a*) The gun did not fire. (*b*) The arrows flew wide. (*c*) The spear was too short. (*d*) The stone missed its target. (*e*) There was a hole in the net. (*f*) Their aim was not good enough. (*g*) The birds were too difficult to hit. Write down the correct answers.

8. When they brought down a pigeon, how do we know that they were not aiming **at any particular pigeon**?

9. Which words or phrases mean: (*a*) saw, or noticed; (*b*) colours; (*c*) a bird of the parrot family; (*d*) tries; (*e*) the middle?

II. A man's home is a **house**. In what do these people live?

1. An Eskimo   2. A soldier   3. A vicar
4. A king   5. A convict   6. An abbot

III. Rewrite the paragraph below, using a word from the list given to fill each of the spaces:

fro	white-sailed	valley	river
sun	together	babbling	sea

The —— stream rippled through the —— until she met with her big sister, the ——. Then —— they rushed towards the ——, where the —— ships darted to and ——, and the water sparkled in the summer ——.

IV. Jill's doll is **pretty**, Pat's is **prettier**, but Sally's is **prettiest**. Fill in the spaces in these sentences in the same way:

1. My share is **small**, your share is ——, but his is the ——.
2. Norah was **clever**, Dora was ——, but Cora was the ——.
3. Tom lives **far** away, Dick lives ——, and Harry lives ——.
4. My hair is **dark**, Judith's is ——, and Janet's is ——.

V. Fill in the spaces below with the correct **sound-words**:

Can you tell the difference between the —— of a lion and the —— of a wolf, or the —— of a sea-gull and the —— of a pigeon? We all know that a cat —— when happy, and —— when unhappy.

TEST 14

I. Read very carefully through the following passage, and then answer the questions.

Long, Long Ago

There was a time in history when this land we now call Britain was not an island. It was joined to the rest of Europe, and hills and forests once stood where the North Sea and the English Channel are today. Then, owing to some great earthquakes, much of the land sank, the sea rushed in, and only the high parts remained above the surface of the water. Before this happened the mountains of Britain—Ben Nevis, Snowdon and others—must have been very high land indeed.

How do we know all this? Fishermen trawling in the North Sea and the English Channel have found in their nets the bones of prehistoric animals that must have been roaming about on what was once dry land. Sabre-toothed tigers, mammoths and other creatures that have disappeared long years ago could not have been paddling about in canoes, could they?

1. What used to be where the North Sea and the Channel are today?
2. What caused much of the land to sink?
3. Which two mountains are named in the story?
4. We know all this is **true**, because: (*a*) It was written down in books at that time. (*b*) It was told by father to son. (*c*) The bones of dry-land animals have been brought to the surface by fishermen. Which?
5. Which two prehistoric animals are named in the story?
6. When did all this happen: (*a*) last year; (*b*) during the last century; (*c*) in the last five hundred years; (*d*) thousands of years ago?

7. Why were the bones of these animals found by **trawling** fishermen: (*a*) because trawl-nets scrape along the sea-bed; (*b*) because trawlers are the only kind of fishing-boat; (*c*) because they use divers to go down to the sea-bed?

8. Sabre-toothed tigers and mammoths are **prehistoric** animals. Does this mean: (*a*) They are still roaming about today in all countries. (*b*) They once lived, but died out thousands of years ago. (*c*) There never were such animals?

II. A **young wolf** is a **cub**. Write down the names for the young of the animals and people listed below:

1. dog   2. fox   3. hen
4. cat   5. swan   6. king

III. From the word **strong** (The man was strong), we can make the word **strength** (The man had great strength).

In the same way, rewrite the sentences below changing the word given before each and putting it in the space.

1. **proud**   She showed great —— in her work.
2. **angry**   You must not show your —— at what he has done.
3. **brave**   He was praised for his ——.
4. **clean**   The visitor noticed the —— of the streets.

IV. Here are six words that describe **how** something is done:

> gracefully   sweetly   swiftly
> bravely   peacefully   quietly

Use one of the words in each of the following sentences:

1. He slept ——.   4. They fought ——.
2. She danced ——.   5. He hummed ——.
3. They sang ——.   6. She ran ——.

V. At what type of shop should I buy the following:

1. beds, chairs, tables   3. bulbs, plants, flowers
2. pumps, tyres, inner-tubes   4. sausages, mince, chops

TEST 15

I. Read very carefully through the following verses, and then answer the questions.

Hiawatha

Down a narrow pass they wandered,
Where a brooklet led them onward,
Where the trail of deer and bison
Marked the soft mud on the margin,
Till they found all further passage
Shut against them, barred securely
By the trunks of trees uprooted,
Lying lengthwise, lying crosswise,
And forbidding further passage.

"We must go back," said the old man,
"O'er the logs we cannot clamber;
Not a woodchuck could get through them,
Not a squirrel clamber o'er them."

H. W. Longfellow

1. Write down the sentences that are **true**: (*a*) They walked down a wide roadway. (*b*) The track was narrow and muddy. (*c*) A stream rippled near at hand. (*d*) The surface was hard and rocky. (*e*) A deep river flowed near by. (*f*) The people were going along quite slowly.
2. What stopped them from going further along the path?
3. How did they know that animals had been along there also?
4. How do we know that the trees had not been **chopped** down?
5. How did the old man say "We cannot climb over these tree-trunks"?
6. How can we tell that this was happening in a foreign country?
7. Which line of the poem tells us that the trees were not **all lying in the same direction?**

8. What words or phrases mean: (*a*) a small brook; (*b*) the edge of the brook?

II. From the word **love** we can make the word **loving**.

Rewrite the sentences below changing the word given before each and putting it in the space.

1. **sense**   You are a very —— person.
2. **pride**   The —— king sat on his throne.
3. **glory**   It was a —— victory.
4. **velvet**   The mole has a —— skin.

III. **Who** does **What?**

1. A **pedlar**   (*a*) rides a bicycle; (*b*) sells things at people's houses; (*c*) interferes with other people.
2. A **steeplejack** (*a*) plays a card game; (*b*) rides horses; (*c*) repairs chimneys and high buildings.
3. A **surgeon**   (*a*) makes things out of serge; (*b*) performs operations; (*c*) catches fish.
4. A **chauffeur**   (*a*) drives a private car; (*b*) does no work at all; (*c*) sells groceries.

IV. Look at these two words: **obey** and **disobey**. By adding **dis** to **obey** the word becomes the exact opposite in meaning.

Now write the **opposites** of these words, using **dis, un, im** or **in**: fair, possible, connect, visible, happy, mortal.

V. Look at these three words: **inform, perform, reform**. Which of them would you write in the space in this sentence? 'The doctor is going to —— an operation.' Answer: **perform.**

Fill the gaps in these sentences, choosing one word each time:

1. **cataract, parapet, minaret.** The canoe was washed over the ——.
2. **complete, compete, consult.** Shall we —— in the sports?
3. **department, compartment, appointment.** There were three empty seats in the next —— of the train.

33

TEST 16

I. Read very carefully through the following passage, and then answer the questions.

The Tea-Party

There was a table set out under a tree in front of the house, and the March Hare and the Hatter were having tea at it. A Dormouse was sitting between them, fast asleep, and the other two were using it as a cushion, resting their elbows on it, and talking over its head. "Very uncomfortable for the Dormouse," thought Alice, "only, as it's asleep, I suppose it doesn't mind."

The table was a large one, but the three were all crowded together at one corner of it. "No room! No room!" they cried together when they saw Alice. "There's **plenty** of room," said Alice indignantly, as she sat down in a large arm-chair at one end of the table.

"Have some wine," the March Hare said. Alice looked around the table, but there was nothing on it but tea.

"I don't see any wine," she remarked.

Lewis Carroll

1. Where was the table placed: (*a*) out of doors; (*b*) in the kitchen; (*c*) in the dining-room; (*d*) in the kitchenette?
2. When Alice arrived, who were already at the table?
3. What did they shout when they saw Alice?
4. What was Alice's reply?
5. What did the March Hare offer Alice to drink: (*a*) a cup of tea; (*b*) a mug of cocoa; (*c*) some wine; (*d*) a beaker of milk?
6. Why couldn't Alice accept the March Hare's offer?
7. The Dormouse was not very comfortable, but the others were. Why was this?
8. Why didn't the Dormouse seem to mind?
9. Why is the word **plenty** printed differently from the other words?

10. Which of these words describe Alice at that moment: cross, pleased, irritated, delighted, dissatisfied, annoyed, vexed, charmed, happy, displeased?

II. Chairs, benches, stools, forms, are all **seats**. Write down a general name for each of these groups:
1. gull, puffin, tern, guillemot
2. ant, bee, wasp, fly
3. London, Paris, Brussels, Madrid
4. franc, lira, rupee, peseta
5. B.B.C., P.T.O., l.b.w., G.P.O.

III. Below is a paragraph. The words in heavy type show that the story is taking place **now**. Change these words so that the story happened **in the past**.

The school party **leaves** the station and **makes** its way down the road. As the children **see** the inviting sea they **shout** for joy and **hurry** to the beach as fast as they **can**. The day **is** hot and they **are** keen to have a bathe.

IV. From the word **lose** we can make the word **loss**.

Rewrite the sentences below, changing the word given before each sentence and putting it in the space.
1. **obey**   I must have complete —— from you all.
2. **invent**   The telephone is a wonderful ——.
3. **succeed**   I look forward to hearing of your ——.
4. **describe** This is a —— of what I saw.

V. Write **is** or **are** in the space in each sentence:
1. Each tyre —— punctured.
2. Their brother and sister —— away from school.
3. Both the Rangers and the Albion —— to be promoted.
4. One of the panes —— broken.

TEST 17

I. Read very carefully through the following passage, and then answer the questions.

Books

John had one shelf in the bookcase for his own books. There were books of adventure and school stories, with gaily-coloured covers. Most of the books contained exciting pictures of hunters fighting battles with hungry wolves or man-eating lions. Others showed spaceships circling the earth, linking up in space, or landing on strange planets.

John knew many of these stories by heart, for he had read them so many times. Yet, every evening he would take one down from the shelf and carry it away to his bedroom, to look at it just as eagerly as if it were a new book. Now and then there were new books to add to the shelf, and his proudest possession was the colourful encyclopedia which he had been given for his birthday.

1. Where did John keep his books?
2. Which kinds of books did he like?
3. In what way were the book covers similar?
4. Write down the sentences that are **true**. The pictures in most of the books were: (*a*) of airmen flying over deserts; (*b*) of fights between hunters and animals; (*c*) of girls playing netball; (*d*) of spaceships and strange planets; (*e*) of famous buildings; (*f*) of girls washing up the tea-things.
5. How can we tell that John knew the contents of many of the books very well?
6. How often did he add new books to his shelf?
7. What was John's proudest possession?
8. What is your proudest possession?
9. What is an **encyclopedia**?

10. John looked at the book **eagerly.** Write down the words and phrases from this list which have a similar meaning to **eagerly**: calmly, all agog, coolly, breathlessly, without much interest, excitedly.

II. When speaking of something **hard,** we may say it is **as hard as iron.**

Choose the correct answers from these.
1. As quick as (*a*) a smash; (*b*) a flash; (*c*) a splash.
2. As slow as (*a*) a tortoise; (*b*) a bus; (*c*) a noise.
3. As busy as (*a*) a wasp; (*b*) a bee; (*c*) a hen.
4. As keen as (*a*) custard; (*b*) mustard; (*c*) marbles.

III. Here are two words, **table** and **spoon.** From these we can make the word **tablespoon.**

From these eight words make four new compound words:

hose	north	wash	fire
water	basin	west	butt

IV. Rewrite the paragraph below, using a word from the list to fill each of the spaces:

horses	eagerly	pence	carved
purses	fair	favourite	left

At the ——, the roundabout with its galloping —— was a great ——. The children —— paid their —— to ride, time after time, the gay, —— animals, until there was no money —— in their ——.

V. From the word **mock** (He began to mock the old man) we can make the word **mocking** (He made a mocking sound).

Now rewrite the sentences below, changing the word given before each and putting it in the space.
1. **study**   Alan was a —— lad.
2. **enjoy**   I hope you will have an —— party.
3. **rebel**   The soldiers are in a —— mood.
4. **decide**   The teacher gave the —— vote.

TEST 18

I. Read very carefully through the following passage, and then answer the questions.

Cowboy and Indians

The lone cowboy leaped from the saddle and took refuge behind the pile of rocks at the edge of the trail. None too soon for, already, arrows were whistling around him, and the war-whoops of the Indians were loud in his ears.

It would take all of 'Quickdraw' Thompson's courage and determination to get him safely out of this peril. Not only was his life at stake, but those of the settlers sleeping peacefully in their log cabins in the lovely valley below. It was so long since there had been an Indian rising that the Palefaces had become careless. Their guns were seldom to hand, and their look-outs had begun to think that they were wasting their time peering out across the prairie for an enemy that never came. The Redmen had chosen the time carefully. Lone Elk had seen to that!

1. Who are the two most important people in the story?
2. Where did the cowboy hide?
3. Why was he only just in time?
4. Why was Thompson named **Quickdraw**: (a) because he was clever at drawing pictures; (b) because he was quick at drawing his gun, and firing; (c) because he sometimes drew a truck loaded with goods?
5. Who were in danger from an Indian attack?
6. Say why Lone Elk had chosen his time carefully.
7. Why were the settlers called **Palefaces**: (a) because they were pale with fear; (b) because they were fighting in the darkness; (c) because their faces were whiter than those of the Redmen?
8. Were the Indians called **Redmen** because: (a) their faces were darker than those of the settlers; (b) the firelight shone on their faces; (c) they were dressed in red?

9. Write down the **one word** that describes: (*a*) how the settlers were sleeping; (*b*) the valley; (*c*) the noise of the arrows.
10. What two words tell us that Thompson was a useful man to have near if you were in trouble?

II. A number of **chicks** together is called a **brood**. What words could be used for:
1. A number of whales
2. A large number of locusts
3. A number of angels
4. A number of oxen drawing a wagon

III. Rewrite these sentences so that they mean **more than one**.
   Example: The **card** lay in the **box**. The **cards** lay in the **boxes**.
1. The child saw the fox.
2. She put the puppy in its basket.
3. The Boy Scout sharpened the sheath-knife.
4. The deer ate the loaf of bread.

IV. There are mistakes in each of these sentences. Rewrite the sentences correctly:
1. He is older than her.
2. Did you hear who ring the bell?
3. He read that poem quite loud.
4. The teacher sung the song at twelve o'clock.
5. The day had just began.

V. From the word **blood** (The blood began to flow) we can make the word **bleed** (He might bleed to death). In the same way, rewrite the sentences below changing the word given before each and putting it in the space.
1. **relief**   Let us try to —— the army in the hills.
2. **thought**   Try to —— harder about it.
3. **provision** It is up to us to —— food for the old people.
4. **mystery**   The conjurer began to —— his audience.

39

TEST 19

I. Read very carefully through the following passage, and then answer the questions.

The Treasure-Box

The ornamental box was taken from the cellar and placed in the centre of the table in the study. Jim's next task was to open the box. Try as he would, he could discover no keyhole, so it seemed clear that a spring of some sort would have to be found.

There were numerous decorations carved on the top and sides: grinning faces, baskets of fruit, sheaves of corn, any of which, when pressed, might cause a panel to slide, or a lid to spring open. There were many failures before Jim's searching fingers finally discovered the correct little carving. Silently, one side of the box collapsed and showed him the secret. There lay the roll of parchment about which so much had been written. It was the treasure-map, the clue to the vast hoard that was hidden somewhere else in the castle.

1. Where was the box: (a) upstairs, in the attic; (b) out in the garden; (c) below, in the cellar; (d) in a garden shed?
2. Where, and in what room, was it then placed?
3. What was Jim's next task?
4. What did he fail to find?
5. What were the carvings that decorated the box?
6. How might one of these carvings lead to the opening of the box?
7. How did the box finally open?
8. What was the secret found inside the box?
9. Why was this so valuable?
10. What words or phrases in the story mean (a) bundles of corn; (b) noiselessly; (c) gave way; (d) decorative; (e) great collection?

11. Write down the sentences that are **true**: (*a*) Jim found the secret in a few seconds. (*b*) The secret was never discovered. (*c*) It was some time before Jim solved the problem. (*d*) The box was quite empty. (*e*) The box contained one thing only. (*f*) The lid of the box finally opened.

II. Rewrite these sentences using **single words** that mean nearly the same as the phrases in heavy type:

1. The children **made fun of** the old man.
2. The man was **without a hair on his head.**
3. Martin was **absolutely tired out** after the race.
4. Jane was **liked by everyone.**

III. The opposite of the word **in** is **out.** Write out these sentences using the opposite of the word in heavy type to fill the space:

1. This park is **public;** that garden is ——.
2. What is the —— to my **question?**
3. —— is the opposite of **plural.**
4. You will have either **success** or —— this time.

IV. Write out in full the **abbreviations** (shortened forms) shown in these sentences:

1. The climbers reached the summit of **Mt.** Everest.
2. The case was tried by Alderman Thompson, **J.P.**
3. They bought the goods from James Harris and **Co. Ltd.**
4. During the war he served with the **R.A.M.C.** as a doctor.

V. From the word **stolen** we can make the word **steal.**

Rewrite the sentences below changing the word given before each and putting it in the space.

1. **decorative**   It is time to —— the dining-room.
2. **strong**   It might be wise to —— the wall.
3. **annoying**   Try not to —— your brother.
4. **married**   The prince is going to —— the peasant girl.

41

TEST 20

I. Read very carefully through the following verses, and then answer the questions.

The Jolly Old Vagabond

One evening when Philip and I were out walking,
We saw in the forest the glow of a fire,
And somehow we knew it was best to stop talking
Whilst pushing through tangles of blackthorn and brier.

And as we drew near, the sound of a fiddle
Came stealing so gaily the branches among,
And there in a clearing, alone in the middle,
We saw someone jigging, and singing a song.

A jolly old man in a coat torn and tattered
Was bowing and scraping, so happy and gay;
His shirt was in ribbons, his hat bent and battered,
But he danced and he sang in a wonderful way.

1. At what time was all this taking place?
2. Why did the children think it was best to stop talking: (*a*) because they knew there were savages about; (*b*) because they were not quite certain what was happening; (*c*) because it was getting near school-time?
3. How can we tell that it was difficult to reach the clearing?
4. Write down the sentences that are **true**: (*a*) They saw a band of musicians practising. (*b*) The sound of a trumpet echoed through the trees. (*c*) There was only one performer present. (*d*) The player was in uniform. (*e*) There was an open space in the forest. (*f*) He was a rather unusual person.
5. The man was doing two things besides playing the fiddle. What were they?
6. Which words tell us that the man was performing **very well indeed?**

7. Look at the words **stealing so gaily the branches among.** Does this mean (*a*) happily taking other people's goods; (*b*) climbing through the trees like a squirrel; (*c*) sounding so pleasantly through the trees?

II. Oak, ash, elm, chestnut are all **trees.** Give a general name for each of the following groups:

1. lance, sword, cutlass, dagger
2. carnation, daisy, buttercup, lily
3. history, geography, arithmetic, handwork
4. barley, maize, wheat, oats
5. butter, eggs, cheese, cream

III. Name these people of whom we read in a book or poem.

1. A chimney sweep who became a water baby.
2. He was a detective with an assistant called Dr. Watson.
3. He went down to Buckingham Palace with Alice.
4. He fought the Doones on Exmoor.
5. He was marooned by Captain Flint, on Treasure Island.

IV. Rewrite the paragraph below using a word from the list to fill each of the spaces:

near Faithful king master fondest servant

An old —— lay sick, and when he found his end was drawing ——, he said: "Let —— John come to me." Now he was the —— that the king was —— of, and he was so called because he had been true to his —— all his life.

V. We call **high and low** a word-double.

Complete these sentences with the correct word-doubles:

1. The defenders fought **tooth and** —— at the gates.
2. The attacking army fought with **might and** ~~Death~~.
3. We must try to make a **rough and** ~~ShGd~~ barrier.
4. They stood together through **thick and** ~~th~~.

TEST 21

I. Read very carefully through the following passage, and then answer the questions.

Karl Katz

A great many years ago there lived in a village at the foot of a mountain a man called Karl Katz. Karl was a goatherd, and every morning he drove his flock to a part of the mountainside where there were patches of good grass. In the evenings, he sometimes thought it too late to drive his flock home, so he used to shut up the animals in a ruin in the woods. The ruin was part of an old castle that had long been deserted, and the walls were high enough to form a fold in which he could count his goats and let them rest for the night. One evening he found that the prettiest goat of his flock had vanished soon after they were driven into the fold. He searched for it everywhere, but in vain.

1. Karl Katz lived (*a*) in a village on the mountain-top; (*b*) in a village half-way up a mountain; (*c*) in a village near the sea; (*d*) in a village right at the foot of a mountain. Which?
2. When did this story happen: (*a*) last year; (*b*) last week; (*c*) a very long time ago?
3. Karl was in charge of (*a*) a flock of goats; (*b*) a herd of cows; (*c*) a flock of sheep; (*d*) a caravan of camels. Which?
4. At what time of day did he drive his animals to feed?
5. What was the ready-made fold he found on the mountainside?
6. When did he sometimes use this place?
7. Which one of his flock was missing?
8. What did he do when he discovered his loss?
9. He drove his flock to certain places: (*a*) because they were near at hand; (*b*) because he was too lazy to go anywhere else; (*c*) because the best grass was to be found there. Which of these?

10. What words or phrases in the story mean: (*a*) a place for keeping goats; (*b*) a number of goats; (*c*) disappeared; (*d*) without succeeding?

II. Here are five sentences from a story, but they are not in the order in which things happened. Write them in the correct order.
1. He tried hard to find the reason for the break.
2. There seemed to be nothing he could do.
3. In the middle of the programme, the radio stopped.
4. After a while he gave it up in despair.
5. David crossed over to the set.

III. MAN is a **masculine** word. Its partner WOMAN is a **feminine** word. In the following sentences write **feminine** words in place of the **masculine** words shown in heavy type:
1. My **uncle** is my **landlord.**
2. The **count** is my **master.**
3. The **monk** became an **abbot.**
4. The Red Indian **brave** and my **nephew** became friends.

IV. **Punctuation marks** (full stops, capital letters, commas, etc.) have been omitted from the following sentences. Rewrite the sentences correctly:
1. once upon a time there were a hare a rabbit and a tortoise
2. hes not tired at the moment
3. its not so much its shape as its size
4. thats not so

V. **Odd man out.** In each of these groups of words, one word is out of place because it has nothing to do with the others.
   Example: boy, girl, lass, woman, **tiger.** **Tiger** is odd man out.
   Find the **odd man out** in these:
1. gaol, prison, goal, jail
2. father, mother, uncle, sister
3. tennis, football, ice-hockey, golf
4. cycle, walk, tramp, march

TEST 22

I. Read very carefully through the following passage, and then answer the questions.

Lost Property

It happened one day aboard the 'Antelope' that Sam, the captain's servant, whilst emptying his master's silver teapot, accidentally dropped the valuable article overboard. He was terrified as to what would happen when the captain found out, so he made up his mind to make things a little easier for himself.

"Sir, is a thing lost when you know where it is?" he asked the skipper.

"Of course it isn't," was the reply. "If you know where it is, it can't be lost."

"Are you quite sure of that, sir?" Sam asked anxiously.

"As sure as I am that this ship is sailing the Pacific," said the captain.

"Well, that makes me very happy indeed," said Sam. "Your silver teapot isn't really lost, for I know where it is. It's at the bottom of the ocean."

1. What was the ship's name, and where was it at the time?
2. What was Sam's job aboard the vessel?
3. What was he doing when the story begins?
4. Write down the sentences that are **true**: (a) Sam was very light-hearted at what had happened. (b) He was in a blue funk. (c) He went about whistling happily. (d) He had no fear of anything. (e) He was very much alarmed. (f) He was in a panic.
5. What was the first question he asked the captain?
6. Why did Sam repeat the question?
7. The captain's answers made Sam feel: pleased, happy, uneasy, light of heart, downhearted, disappointed, down in the dumps. Write down the words or phrases that are **true**.

46

II. **Soldier** is to **army** as **sailor** is to ——.   Answer: **navy.**

1. **Oil** is to **well** as **coal** is to ——.
2. **Eleven** is to **cricket** as **fifteen** is to ——.
3. **I** is to **me** as **we** is to ——.
4. **Come** is to **go** as **here** is to ——.

III. Give the answers to these **crossword-puzzle clues.**

1. To frisk and jump.   G – MB – –
2. Quietness.   P – – CE
3. A sound made in pain.   G – – – N
4. A part of something.   P – – CE

IV. Write down the answers to the following questions:

1. What would you expect to find in a wardrobe?
2. Give the name of a place where many rooks build their nests.
3. Where might you hear a cry of "Fares, please!"?
4. What is the work of a glazier?
5. On what would one play a game of golf?
6. To what kind of shop should I go to buy a chisel?

V. When we say that we have 'thrown up the sponge', we mean that we have given up the fight.   This is an **everyday expression.**

   In the following, choose the phrase that means nearly the same as the everyday expression:

1. To **bite the dust** means: (*a*) to fall and swallow a mouthful of dust; (*b*) to be defeated, or killed; (*c*) to test soil.
2. To **turn the tables** means: (*a*) to move the furniture around; (*b*) to learn one's tables at arithmetic; (*c*) to overcome one's enemies, after losing for a while.
3. To **send to Coventry** means: (*a*) to refuse to have anything to do with a certain person; (*b*) to act the play about Lady Godiva; (*c*) to buy a motor-car from Coventry.

TEST 23

I. Read very carefully through the following passage, and then answer the questions.

The Boastful Miller

By the side of a wood, in a distant country, ran a fine stream of water, and upon this stream there stood a mill. The miller's house was close by, and the miller had a very beautiful daughter. The miller was so proud of her that one day he told the king of the land, who used to come and hunt in the wood, that his daughter could spin gold out of straw.

Now, this king was very fond of money, and when he heard the miller's boast, his greediness was aroused and he sent for the girl to be brought before him. Then he led her to a chamber in his palace where there was a great heap of straw. He gave her a spinning-wheel, and said, "All this straw must be spun into gold before morning, as you love your life."

1. How do we know that the country was very far away?
2. What did the miller claim his daughter could do?
3. Why was the king in the wood?
4. The king had one great fault: (a) He was cruel to his subjects. (b) He was too fond of money. (c) He loved eating and drinking. Which of these is true?
5. What task did the king set the miller's daughter to do?
6. When was the task to be completed?
7. The man and his daughter lived (a) in a mansion near the sea; (b) in a thatched cottage in a village; (c) in a house near the mill on the banks of a stream. Which?
8. The miller's daughter was (a) good to look at; (b) unpleasant and ugly; (c) not very attractive. Which?
9. How did the father earn his living: (a) by selling firewood to the people who lived near by; (b) by guiding travellers through the woods; (c) by grinding corn into flour?

10. Write down the words or phrases in the story that mean: (a) 'If you wish to remain alive'; (b) room; (c) claim.

II. **Sound-words** are missing from these sentences. Choose suitable words to fill the spaces:
1. The logs were —— on the fire.
2. The kettle was ——.
3. Ann's skirt —— as she crossed the room.
4. The shutters were —— in the wind.

III. Write these **heavenly bodies** in alphabetical order:

Pluto	Venus	Mars	Uranus
Neptune	Saturn	Jupiter	Mercury
	Earth	Asteroid	

IV. **Choosing suitable words**

1. Here are four **nouns**: chair, witch, fox, mountain.

And here are four **adjectives**: comfortable, cunning, snow-capped, ugly.

Write the words together in suitable pairs.

2. Here are four other **adjectives**: humble, underground, flowery, well-filled.

And here are the four **nouns**: stream, larder, peasant, border.

Write the words together in suitable pairs.

V. Some words have a similar sound, but are spelt differently.

Example: The **plane** flew into the sky. The army marched across the **plain.**

In the sentences below, choose the correct word from those inside the brackets:

1. The Arabs rode their camels across the (**dessert, desert**).
2. The prisoner confessed his (**guilt, gilt**).
3. The fishmonger sells (**plaice, place**).
4. Have you a car for (**hire, higher**)?

TEST 24

I. Read very carefully through the following passage, and then answer the questions.

On Treasure Island

Next morning the work of getting the treasure aboard began. I was kept busy packing the money into canvas bags. It took us three days, but at last the bars and coins were safely stowed away in the cabin.

We had seen nothing of the three pirates all this time, but we heard them singing and shouting as if they were drunk, or mad. A meeting was held, and it was decided that we must leave them on the island. We landed a good stock of powder and shot, tools, clothing, a sail, medicines, some rope, and a case of tobacco. Then we weighed anchor, and stood off the island. The three must have been watching us, for as we rounded the point we saw them kneeling on the sand with their arms raised, as if asking for mercy.

R. L. Stevenson

1. Read through these sentences, and then write down those that are **true**: (*a*) The treasure was being put into a cave. (*b*) It was being taken aboard ship. (*c*) It was being stowed away in a bank. (*d*) There were many jewelled swords and daggers. (*e*) There were many pearls and ornaments. (*f*) There were thousands of coins, and gold and silver bars.
2. How can we tell that there was a great deal of treasure?
3. At the meeting, what did they decide to do with the pirates?
4. What did they leave behind on the island (*a*) for the pirates' health; (*b*) for hunting; (*c*) for smoking?
5. The ship **weighed anchor.** Does this mean: (*a*) The sailors found the weight of the anchor. (*b*) They cut the anchor-rope, and let the ship drift. (*c*) The anchor was hauled up and taken aboard?

6. Why did the sailors think the pirates were asking for mercy?
7. The treasure was (*a*) stored in bags made of canvas; (*b*) carried in leather wallets; (*c*) packed away in wooden cases. Which?

II. **Now** and **cow** are rhyming words. They have the same sound. Write these twelve words in pairs, so that they rhyme.

tier	sage	thyme	gnu	role	gauge
flung	goal	pier	climb	flew	tongue

III. Look at this word—**near.** Now look at the three words inside the bracket—(close, distant, far). The word nearest in meaning to **near** is **close,** so we choose that.

Now do the same with these, choosing **one word** each time:

1. **purchase**   (steal, buy, hide)
2. **valley**   (glen, roadway, garden)
3. **ate**   (refused, consumed, wasted)
4. **plump**   (angry, fat, noisy)

IV. Choose, from the words in brackets, the most suitable word to finish the line of poetry:

> Two little blackbirds singing in the (**hedge, morn, sun**)
> One flew away and then there was one;
> One little blackbird, very black and (**shy, tall, brave**)
> He flew away and then there was the wall.
> One little brick wall lonely in the (**field, garden, rain**)
> Waiting for the blackbirds to come and sing again.

V. Look at the word FIRE. It need not be a **coal** fire or an **oil** fire, and it need not be **large** or **small.** But there must be **heat.**

Choose one word from those in the brackets that **always** has to do with the word before the bracket:

1. **husband**   (house, wife, motor-car)
2. **house**   (fire-place, door, cellar)
3. **tree**   (nest, roots, conkers)
4. **boot**   (laces, sole, buttons)

TEST 25

I. Read very carefully through the following verses, and then answer the questions.

Robin Hood

When Robin Hood was about twenty years old,
He happened to meet Little John,
A jolly, brisk blade, right for the trade,
For he was a lusty young man.

Though he was called Little, his limbs they were large,
And his stature was seven foot high;
Whenever he came, they quaked at his name,
For soon he would make them fly.

How they 'came acquainted I'll tell you in brief,
If you will but listen awhile.

1. At that time Robin was (*a*) a boy; (*b*) an elderly man; (*c*) a young man; (*d*) a very old man. Which is true?
2. What words tell us that Robin did not go on purpose to meet Little John?
3. **A jolly brisk blade.** Does this mean (*a*) a useful young man; (*b*) a very sharp knife; (*c*) a trusty sword; (*d*) a pretty piece of grass?
4. How can we tell that **Little** was not a true description of Little John?
5. People **quaked at his name.** Does this mean: (*a*) laughed out loud; (*b*) they shivered with fright; (*c*) they had never heard of him?
6. **Right for the trade.** Does this mean for; (*a*) selling fruit and vegetables; (*b*) driving a stage-coach; (*c*) fighting and duelling; (*d*) cutting wood?
7. **I'll tell you in brief.** What does **in brief** mean?

8. **How they 'came acquainted.** Does this mean: (*a*) how they danced and sang; (*b*) how they met one another; (*c*) where they were born?

II. The words in each of the following are in wrong order. Rearrange them to make sentences.
1. Ball the window broke whose?
2. The sweet ate last Jack.
3. The gold perhaps will show the miser us.
4. A grate the fire in burned.

III. Each of the answers to the following clues begins with the letters MON. Write down the words.
1. We buy things with it.   MON - -
2. A king.   MON - - - -
3. Where monks live.   MON - - - - - -
4. One who helps the teacher.   MON - - - -

IV. The word **file** has more than one meaning. It may mean 'a tool for smoothing or cutting metal'; it may mean 'a line of soldiers'; or it may mean 'a container for papers'.
   Write down the words that fit in with the following descriptions:
1. Part of a tree; part of the human body; a piece of luggage.
2. Heroic; Red Indian warrior.
3. Part of a ship; strict or rather fierce.
4. We might use this to light a fire; a contest between teams.

V. The words in the first bracket mean something similar.
   Choose a **word** of similar meaning from those in the second bracket.
   Example: (**first, foremost, head**)—(final, **leading**, prettiest)
1. (vanish, perish, disappear)—(last, fade, continue)
2. (stake, post, pillar)—(trench, ditch, column)
3. (lead, start, begin)—(commence, end, destroy)
4. (fraction, piece, part)—(total, portion, addition)

TEST 26

I. Read very carefully through the following passage, and then answer the questions.

Games

The children played many games in the busy roadway and on the pavement of the street in which they lived. The favourite for girls was Hopscotch, but this meant that untidy chalk marks were left behind, and there they stayed until the rain came and washed them out. The boys liked playing noisier games such as 'Release', or 'Last across the road', in which there was a great deal of shouting, and some danger.

The smaller girls sat in their own doorways nursing dolls, or dressing and undressing them. The dolls always had names like 'Belinda' or 'Millicent Jane', for there never seemed to be any boy-dolls.

Some boys played football or cricket. Boys and girls would join in the game called 'Statues', in which they had to stand as still as possible in a queer position, pretending to be carved from stone.

1. How can you tell that these children lived in a town, and not in the country?
2. Why was hopscotch an **untidy** game?
3. What, finally, got rid of the chalking?
4. Why were **Release** and **Last across the road** noisy and dangerous games?
5. Why were doorways suitable places for playing with dolls: (a) because they were the doorways of dolls' houses; (b) because they were just off the busy pavements; (c) because no one lived in the houses?
6. How could you tell when the children were playing 'Statues'?
7. Choose a suitable title from these: (a) Grown-ups' Behaviour. (b) Children's Pleasures. (c) Animals' Antics.

II. We speak of **a** girl and **a** street, but **an** egg and **an** iron. Write **a** or **an** in the spaces in these sentences:

1. He put —— iris and —— aster with —— lily.
2. She bought —— book, —— pen and —— atlas.
3. —— wren is smaller than —— owl or —— albatross.
4. The juice of —— orange makes —— good drink.

III. Complete these **proverbs** or well-known sayings:

1. Fine feathers —— —— ——.
2. First come, —— ——.
3. It's a long lane —— —— —— ——.
4. Let sleeping dogs ——.

IV. From the words **inside the bracket** in each sentence, write down the one word that is nearest in meaning to the word in front of the sentence.

Example: **difficult.** The sum is (easy, **hard,** simple).

1. **hastened**   They (strolled, hurried, walked) to school.
2. **wicked**   The man behaved in an (odd, evil, innocent) way.
3. **healthy**   That plant looks quite (fragile, hardy, weak).
4. **news**   What (pictures, drawings, information) have you?

V. Rewrite this paragraph beginning each **proper noun** with a **capital letter.**

There was great excitement at loamville when the maharajah of swound visited the town. john brown arranged a concert at the majestic theatre, and his highness presented certificates to pupils of fairview primary school for good work in national savings. The orchestra played morning by grieg, and the loamville festival choir sang handel's messiah.

TEST 27

I. Read very carefully through the following passage, and then answer the questions.

The Changeling Child

A mother once had her child stolen from her by the elves. Instead, they placed in the cradle a creature with a large head and staring eyes that would do nothing but eat and drink. So the mother went to one of her neighbours and asked her advice. The neighbour told her to carry the changeling into the kitchen and seat it on the hearth, then to light a fire and boil some water in two eggshells. This would make the changeling laugh, and it would be all over with him. The mother obeyed.

As she put the eggshells with the water in them on the fire, the little gnome-child began to laugh. At once a company of elves came crowding into the kitchen, bringing with them the woman's own child. Then they took up the changeling and disappeared with him.

1. Who stole the baby from the mother?
2. From where did they steal it?
3. How did the mother know that it was not her baby that was left?
4. The mother went (a) to her own father and mother; (b) to someone living near by; (c) to the king of the country. Which of these?
5. The creature was called a changeling because: (a) It often changed its shape. (b) It got out of the cradle and ran about the room. (c) The elves had exchanged it for a real baby. Which?
6. What four things was the mother told to do?
7. Why did she do these things?
8. Which of these came into the kitchen: (a) a number of pixies; (b) a crowd of men and women; (c) a band of robbers?

9. What were they carrying with them?

10. What finally happened to the visitors and the changeling?

II. France, Belgium, Holland and Spain are all **countries.** Write down a general name for each of these groups:

1. goose, turkey, chicken, duck
2. grocer, butcher, greengrocer, fishmonger
3. mammoth, brontosaurus, pterodactyl, sabre-toothed tiger
4. strawberry, raspberry, loganberry, gooseberry

III. In each case, rearrange the letters to make the name of an article of food. Example: GURAS becomes SUGAR.

1. C O B N A   2. T U T B E R
3. D R A B E   4. O C O A C

IV. Write down this passage as it should be written, in verse. Begin each line with a **capital letter.**

And we will sit upon the rocks, and see the shepherds feed their flocks, by sunny rivers to whose falls, melodious birds sing madrigals.

V. Beginning with the word BAD, and changing only one letter at a time, we can make the word COT.

Example: BAD, CAD, CAT, COT.

In the same way, change the word PAGE into the word BOOK.

PAGE

1. Anger.	– – – –
2. An event at the sports.	– – – –
3. A framework of bars.	– – – –
4. Found in and on earth.	– – – –
5. A black bird.	– – – –

BOOK

TEST 28

I. Read very carefully through the following passage, and then answer the questions.

The Zoo

Before a zoo can be set up, someone must catch animals to go in it. This is a very difficult and dangerous business. To trap a baby elephant, a net or large bamboo cage is put up in the jungle. The animal is enticed into it by means of sugar-cane or bananas.

For lions, tigers and other ferocious man-eaters an iron cage is needed, and a bait of freshly-killed meat. Crocodiles are very awkward to handle. I heard of one that was carried about in a cricket-bag. Large snakes are more easily dealt with after they have had a good meal. Then they behave like human-beings who have over-eaten, I suppose. Smaller, more deadly snakes are taken by slipping bags over their heads. Catching birds or butterflies would be more to my liking.

1. What has to happen before there can be animals in a zoo?
2. What is the best trap for an elephant?
3. What bait would you need?
4. What makes the best trap for a lion?
5. Why would a crocodile be difficult to handle: (a) because it lives in a foreign land; (b) because it cannot understand English; (c) because it has sharp teeth and a powerful tail?
6. Why was the cricket-bag a suitable carrier?
7. When is the best time to catch a large snake?
8. Is this because: (a) It crawls happily into the trap. (b) It then becomes sleepy. (c) It wishes to rush about?
9. Why should a deadly snake have a bag slipped over its head: (a) because it likes to wear that type of thing; (b) because it cannot see in the dark; (c) because it would not be able to use its deadly fangs?

10. Why would the writer be happier catching birds or butter-flies?
11. What words or phrases in the story mean: (*a*) fierce or savage; (*b*) difficult?

II. What are the names of these people whom we read of in a famous book or poem?

1. He never would shut the door.
2. He was kidnapped, and later met Alan Breck.
3. She was burnt at the stake.
4. The three companions on Coral Island were Ralph Rover, Jack Martin and ——.
5. We had to be quiet when he was saying his prayers.

III. A **splinter** is a very small piece **of wood.** Here are some other small amounts:

> ear   posy   lock   moment

Choose the correct ones to use with the following words:

> flowers   corn   time   hair

IV. Below are pairs of sentences. Join each pair by using one of the following words: **which, whom, who, whose.** You may have to rearrange the words in some cases.

1. The guard blew the whistle. He is quite old.
2. I found the cricketer. His score was the highest.
3. Here is the car. It was stolen.
4. Look at the girl. You scolded her.

V. Complete the words below by adding **ary** or **ery,** whichever is correct:

1. He taught in a **prim** --- school.
2. Mary went to a **second** --- school.
3. The **scen** --- was magnificent.
4. Modern **machin** --- was put into the factory.

TEST 29

I. Read very carefully through the following passage, and then answer the questions.

The Circus

The circus had come to town. Through the High Street the happy procession made its way to the common, led by the bandsmen in their gay uniforms. The trumpets and trombones gleamed in the sun, and the noise of the drum could be heard many streets away.

Koko, the chief clown, came next with cartwheels and handsprings to please everyone. His face was painted white, but his mouth was scarlet. His pointed hat always stayed on his head, although he seemed to spend most of his time upside-down. A string of elephants lumbered along, trunk to tail. Each had on its back a rider dressed as an Indian rajah, with silken jacket, and turban decorated with jewels. Of course, the gems were only imitation ones, but they looked real.

1. Where was the circus going to pitch?
2. Through what street did it have to pass?
3. Who were at the head of the procession?
4. How do we know that the band was playing loudly?
5. What two things could Koko do well?
6. How was Koko's face different from most people's faces?
7. Why was it surprising that Koko's hat stayed on his head?
8. Why does the story say **a string** of elephants?
9. Why were the riders dressed like Indian rajahs: (*a*) because they were the only ones who could ride elephants; (*b*) because Indian rajahs sometimes ride elephants; (*c*) because they were all named Rajah?
10. Why were the jewels imitations: (*a*) because real ones would have been too big; (*b*) because real ones would have cost too much; (*c*) because elephants do not like real ones?

II. Below is a story. The words in heavy type show that it is taking place **now**. Change these words so that the story happened in the **past**.

Today the sun **shines** brightly, and the birds **sing**. I **go** to the lakeside and **dive** into the clear water, where the rowing boats **glide** smoothly. Tom and I **paddle** across to the place where the train **begins** its journey. The guard **waves** to us.

III. Look at this sentence: Where is Bettys doll? The **apostrophe** is missing.

The sentence should have been: Where is Betty's doll?

Write out these sentences, putting the **apostrophe** in its correct place.

1. Jacks desk is broken.
2. The foxs cub is loose.
3. The foxes cubs are loose.
4. John Browns dog is a spaniel.
5. Pams brooch is better than Marys.

IV. Look at these two sentences:
(*a*) The girl said: "I am eleven."
(*b*) The girl said that she was eleven.

In the first sentence the girl **speaks the words**. In the second sentence she does not actually speak. Change the following sentences so that the people are **actually speaking**.

1. The mate said that the boat was sinking.
2. He asked the way to the football ground.
3. The duchess told the servant to clear the table.
4. The pirate ordered him to walk the plank.

V. When we hear the word **knife** we often think of the word **fork**. Write down the words which go with the following:

1. Cowboys and —— 4. Floor and ——
2. Black and —— 5. Saddle and ——
3. Snakes and ——

61

TEST 30

I. Read very carefully through the following verses, and then answer the questions.

Fairy Song

Come follow, follow me,
You fairy elves that be,
Which circle on the green;
Come follow me, your queen.
Hand in hand, let's dance a round,
For this place is fairy ground.

When mortals are at rest,
And snorting in their nest,
Unheard and unespied,
Through keyholes we do glide;
Over tables, over stools, and shelves,
We trip it with our fairy elves.

1. Who is singing the song: (*a*) a mortal; (*b*) a giant; (*c*) a goblin; (*d*) a fairy; (*e*) an ogre?
2. When is the dancing going to take place?
3. When mortals are **snorting in their nest.** Does this mean: (*a*) They are quarrelling. (*b*) They are reading. (*c*) They are snoring. (*d*) They are sleeping peacefully?
4. How would the elves enter the rooms of the mortals?
5. **Circle on the green.** Does this mean: (*a*) ride cycles that are green in colour; (*b*) dance in a circle on the grass; (*c*) play with hoops, whilst wearing green clothes?
6. What does the word **nest** mean in the poem?
7. What words or phrases in the poem mean: (*a*) unseen; (*b*) move very silently?
8. **We trip it.** Which does the phrase mean: (*a*) go on a trip, or holiday; (*b*) stumble over the furniture; (*c*) dance lightly?
9. What is the difference between: (*a*) Let's dance a round. (*b*) Let's dance around?

II. What are the names of these people or creatures whom we read of in famous books?

1. He discovered the treasure chamber of the Forty Thieves.
2. She had three sisters: Meg, Beth and Amy.
3. They were all members of the Swiss Family ——.
4. He tied himself to the leg of a giant bird.

III. A snail's home is its **shell**. What are the homes of these creatures?

1. spider	4. dog
2. pig	5. bee
3. wild rabbit	6. sheep

IV. Rewrite the paragraph below, using a word from the list to fill each of the spaces.

hollow	inn	tree	home
sleep	feathers	carrying	gold

He set to work to cut down the ——. When it fell he found, in a —— under the roots, a goose with —— of pure ——. He took it up and, —— it under his arm, he went to a little —— by the roadside. Here he decided to —— for the night on his way ——.

V. **Odd man out.** In each of these groups of words, one word is out of place because it has nothing to do with the others.

Example: pig, horse, **lion**, sheep, cow. **Lion** is odd man out, because it is the only wild animal of the five.

Find the **odd man out** in these:

1. potatoes, wheat, oats, rye
2. army, brigade, fleet, regiment
3. knight, puck, queen, pawn
4. rope, twine, glue, string